What the Ladybird Heard

MAKE AND DO BOOK

Based on the picture book by

Julia Donaldson • Lydia Monks

MACMILLAN CHILDREN'S BOOKS

Hints and Tips to Read With a Grown-Up

Are you ready to get creative? There are lots of fun ideas in this book for brilliant things to make and do. Before you get started, read through these hints and tips with a grown-up.

* Have a grown-up with you at all times when doing any of the activities in this book, and make sure you ask for help if you find any of the steps a bit tricky.

* Be very careful when using scissors, and always check with a grown-up first to make sure they're not too sharp and are safe for you to use.

* Before you start an activity, read the instructions together so you can make sure you have everything you need.

* Some of these craft ideas can get messy, so wear an apron or old clothes that your grown-up doesn't mind you getting dirty. It's a good idea to tie your hair back if it's long to stop it getting in the way.

* It's best to work on a wipe-clean surface, but you could always cover the floor and table with used newspapers or an old cloth, too.

* Remember to wash your hands after using paint, glue or anything else that might make a mess.

* Arts and crafts can be a great way to reuse things that you might otherwise throw away. For example, you could cut up an old cereal box instead of buying new card. On the next page, you can see a list of some things you might need for the activities in this book. Why not ask your friends and family to help you start saving them?

Things to collect:

Wooden clothes pegs
Egg boxes
Leftover wrapping paper or tissue paper
Lolly sticks
Coloured wool

Paper cups
Plastic milk bottle tops
Toilet roll tubes
Rubber bands
Cereal boxes

How to use your templates:

You can find some drawings on the back of your sticker pages so you can make templates that will help you with some of the activities in this book, like the Clucking Hen on pages 14 and 15. Here's how to make your templates:

1 Lay a piece of thin paper or tracing paper over the outline on the back of your sticker page. Draw over it with a pencil.

2 Carefully cut out your drawing and glue it to a piece of card.

3 Now cut around your drawing so that you have a piece of card the same shape as the original outline. This is your template! You can draw around it as many times as you like.

How to use your stickers:

There are two pages of stickers at the end of this book. They have been specially designed for you to decorate the things you make, but you might prefer to draw your own decorations.

Now you're all set to start – so roll up your sleeves, get out your pens and pencils and have fun!

Lots of Ladybirds

Use pegs, pebbles and paints to create
loads of lovely ladybirds!

You will need:

Smooth stones or pebbles
Red and white acrylic paint
A paintbrush
A black washable marker pen

Painted Pebbles

What to do:

1 Paint your pebble red all over and
leave to dry.

2 Colour a black section at the top to make a
face, then paint on eyes or use stickers
from your sticker sheet.

3 Draw a black line down the middle to make
wings, and add black spots.

4 Repeat these steps to make more
pebble ladybirds!

Hello there! Let's be friends.

Peg Ladybirds

You will need:

Clothes pegs (one for each
   ladybird)
A pencil
A sheet of red card
Safety scissors
A black pen
Black pipe cleaners
Glue

What to do:

1 Use the pencil to draw an
   oval shape on the red card,
   about 4–5cm long, then cut it
   out. (You can trace the ladybird
   on the back of your sticker sheet.)

2 Draw a black line down the middle to make
   wings, then add spots and a face. You can
   use eye stickers or stick on googly eyes.

3 Cut pipe cleaners into shorter lengths and
   stick them to the back of your ladybird to
   make legs and antennae. Glue your ladybird
   to the flat side of a peg.

4 Repeat to make more ladybirds. You can
   use them as decorations, bookmarks,
   or clip them on to whatever you like.

Tips, Tricks and Twists

* How about cutting some leaves out of green paper for your ladybirds
   to sit on? There's a template on the back of your sticker sheet.

* You can make other pebble minibeasts too – try painting yellow
   and black stripes and adding tissue paper wings for a bee, or using
   different colours for a bright, shimmery beetle.

* Hang up a long piece of string in your bedroom and use your
   ladybird pegs to clip on all your favourite cards and drawings!

Prize Rosette

"We can't let them steal the fine prize cow!"
Make this colourful rosette just like the fine prize cow wears.

You will need:

2 A4 sheets of thin
   coloured card
Safety scissors
Double-sided
   sticky tape
Colouring pens
   or pencils
Glue
Sticky tape
A safety pin or
   badge pin

What to do:

1 Fold a sheet of card in half so the long sides meet, then unfold it and cut along the fold to make two pieces.

2 Take one of your pieces of card and fold up one of the short ends about 1cm.

3 Turn the card over and fold the tab you just made back on itself to make another. Keep going like this until the whole piece is folded like an accordion.

4 Fold the second piece of card in the same way.

5 Take the first folded piece and bend it in the middle. Use double-sided tape to stick the middle strips together, then fan the piece out to make a semi-circle.

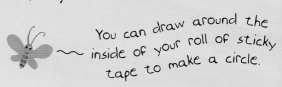

6 Repeat step 5 with your second piece of folded card. Use double-sided tape to stick the edges of the pieces together to make a circle.

7 Cut two circles from your second piece of card, each about 5cm across. Glue one circle on each side of your rosette, in the middle. Write whatever you like on the front circle – how about 'First Prize', 'No. 1', or your name?

You can draw around the inside of your roll of sticky tape to make a circle.

8 Cut two long thin rectangles from your leftover card. Cut a V shape into the end of each one to make them look like ribbons, then tape or glue them to the back of your rosette.

Copy the shape in the picture. ~

9 Ask a grown-up to help you use a piece of tape to stick the safety pin to the back of your rosette (the part that opens should be on the outside), or glue on a badge pin if you have one. Now your rosette is ready to wear!

Tips, Tricks and Twists

❋ Remember that the pin is sharp – always ask your grown-up to pin it on for you.

❋ If you want a different message on your rosette, just make a new card circle and stick it on top of the old one.

❋ You can write anything you like on the middle part. How about making rosettes as prizes for your friends or family? Write a different message on each one, such as 'No. 1 Mum!' or 'Best Friend'.

Farmyard Cress Eggheads

Make farmyard animals from egg shells, then grow real cress to make crazy hair.

You will need:

6 eggs
A glass bowl
Colouring pens or paints
An empty egg box
Safety scissors
18 cotton wool balls
Water
Cress seeds

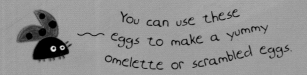

You can use these eggs to make a yummy omelette or scrambled eggs.

What to do:

1 Ask a grown-up to crack each egg on the rim of the glass bowl to remove the top, leaving the bottom two-thirds of the shell intact. Tip the inside of each egg into the bowl. (Don't eat any egg while it's raw, and wash your hands after this step.)

2 Ask your grown-up to gently wash out the inside of each egg shell, being careful not to crack it. Leave them to dry.

3 Now it's time to decorate your egg shells to look like animals. First paint them all over, then add a face near the top of each one. Be gentle so you don't break the shells.

4 Take your egg box and cut off the top.

5 Cut the bottom section in half lengthways, so you have two rows of three egg holders.

6 Carefully place each of your egg shells in an egg holder. Put three cotton wool balls in each shell.

7 Drip 8–10 drops of water on to the top of the cotton wool in each shell, then sprinkle on several cress seeds.

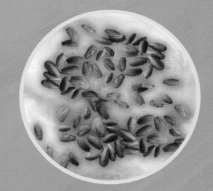

8 Place your egg shells somewhere sunny, such as a kitchen windowsill. Every couple of days sprinkle on a few drops of water. In a few days you will see cress hair starting to grow!

When the cress is about 5cm high you can snip it off and put it in sandwiches or a salad.

Tips, Tricks and Twists

⭐ How about gluing some cotton wool on to an egg shell to make a sheep, or coloured craft feathers for a hen?

⭐ You can make more eggheads with any faces you like – try drawing your friends or family!

⭐ Try putting your eggs in different places. What happens to the cress if it gets lots of sunlight? What about if it's in a shadier spot?

Paper Plate Duck Pond

Once upon a farm lived a fat red hen,
A duck in a pond and a goose in a pen.
This farmyard pond has a duck who really swims!

You will need:

A paper plate
Blue paint
A paintbrush
Glue
A sheet of green A4 card
Safety scissors
Green tissue paper
A small piece of
  plain card
A paperclip
Colouring pens
  and pencils
Sticky tape
A lolly stick
Magnetic tape

What to do:

1 Paint the top of your paper plate blue all over and leave to dry.

2 Cut your sheet of green card in half lengthways. Take one half and cut slits all the way along the long side, each about 3cm long.

3 Cut your length of card into two roughly equal pieces. Push back the tabs, then bend each piece into a curve and glue the tabs to the underside of your paper plate.

4 When the glue has dried, turn your plate back over so it stands up on the card pieces. This is your pond!

5   Scrunch up pieces of green tissue paper and glue them around the edge of your pond. Cut out lilypads from your leftover green card and stick them on, too. You can use the template on the back of your sticker sheet.

6   Take your plain card and draw the outline of a duck. Cut it out, then use pens or pencils to draw details on both sides and colour it in.

You can copy or trace the duck outline on the back of your sticker sheet.

7   Ask a grown-up to unbend a paperclip so the two halves are at a right angle. Use sticky tape to stick one half to the back of your duck. Stand your duck on the pond using the other half.

8   Cut about 2cm of magnetic tape and stick it to the end of a lolly stick. Hold the lolly stick under the plate and move it about to make your duck magically swim!

Tips, Tricks and Twists

✸ Make more ducks and magnetic sticks by repeating steps 6 to 8.

✸ Add extra duck pond decorations from your sticker sheet.

Dotty Decorations

The little spotty ladybird, who never before had said a word . . .
Try three ways of making spotty ladybird patterns,
then decorate whatever you like.

You will need:

3–4 sheets of red A4 paper
Safety scissors
Glue
Red and black acrylic paint
A paintbrush
A saucer or paper plate
Black tissue paper
A pencil
A piece of black paper
A hole punch

What to do:

1 Gather some objects you would like to decorate with ladybird spots. How about a little notebook, a flowerpot for your favourite plant, or reusing empty boxes or tubs to keep your treasures in?

2 Make your object red – wrap it in red paper and glue down the edges, or paint it red with acrylic paint and leave to dry. Now choose how you want to add your spots from the different ways on these pages.

Spotty Fingerprints

1 Pour a little black paint on to a saucer or paper plate.

2 Dip your finger in the paint then press it firmly on to your red surface. Lift it off to see your spotty fingerprint.

3 Add more fingerprint spots until your red surface is covered, then leave to dry.

Tissue Polka Dots

1 Cut a piece of tissue paper into a 4cm x 4cm square. Fold it in half then half again. Now fold it in half two more times, so you have a much smaller square.

2 Draw a circle in the middle of the square, then carefully cut it out. You've made lots of circles! Use glue to stick them to your red surface.

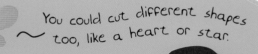

You could cut different shapes too, like a heart or star.

Hole Punch Spots

1 Use the hole punch to punch lots of holes in the black paper. Ask a grown-up to take the bottom off the hole punch to reveal lots of little black dots!

2 Use glue to stick your black dots all over your red surface.

Clucking Hen

And the cow said, "MOO!"
and the hen said, "CLUCK!"
This fat red hen makes a real clucking noise,
just like the hen on the farm!

You will need:

A large yoghurt pot
String or twine
 (about 50cm)
A kitchen sponge
Paints
A paintbrush
Safety scissors
An A4 sheet of red card
Glue
A small dish of water

What to do:

1 Ask a grown-up to poke a small hole in the bottom of the yoghurt pot (a skewer works best for this).

2 Make a knot in one end of your string then thread the string through the hole, so the knot is on the outside of the yoghurt pot.

3 Tie the loose end of the string tightly around the middle of the kitchen sponge.

4 Now it's time to make your pot look like a hen. Paint it red and let the paint dry. Add some yellow feathers, too.

5 Cut a head, wings and beak out of red card and glue them on, then paint the beak yellow. You can copy or trace the templates on the back of your sticker sheet, and add eyes from your sticker sheet or use googly eyes.

6 To make your hen cluck, dip the sponge in the water to make it damp then squeeze out any excess water. Fold the sponge over the string. Holding the hen's body in your other hand, drag the sponge along the string in quick, short movements. Your chicken should make clucking noises!

Don't pull too hard, or the string might come off.

Tips, Tricks and Twists

✸ Nylon string works well for this, but you can use thick cotton string or embroidery thread as well.

✸ Try using different sized empty containers to make a whole group of hens!

✸ Tear paper into thin strips and scrunch it together to make a nest for your hen to sit on.

Arty Animals

A woolly sheep, a hairy hog . . .
Use different art materials to create these cute farmyard animals.

You will need:

Cotton wool balls
Glue
An A4 sheet of
   plain paper
Black paper or card
Safety scissors
Colouring pens
   or paints

Cotton Wool Sheep

1 Dot glue on to cotton wool balls and stick them to a sheet of paper in an oval shape to make the sheep's body.

2 Draw a head and legs on your black card. Cut them out and glue them on to your sheep.

3 Draw or paint eyes or add stickers from your sticker sheet. Add a smile, too!

You will need:

An A4 sheet of
  coloured paper
Colouring pens
Black and white paints
2 sponges
A paper plate
Safety scissors

Sponge Print Cow

1 Draw the outline of a cow on your piece of paper.

2 Pour some white paint on to the paper plate. Dip a sponge in the paint then press it on to your cow's body. Repeat until the body is covered, then leave to dry.

3 Pour some black paint on to your paper plate. Dip your second sponge in the paint then dab it on to your cow to add small splodges all over. Leave to dry.

4 Draw on a face and add horns and hooves, too.

You can copy the outlines on the back of your sticker sheet.

Tips, Tricks and Twists

* Make a hairy hog by drawing its body then gluing on short lengths of pink wool.

* Why not paint or draw a farmyard scene on a big sheet of paper then cut out and add your animals?

* You could also punch holes in the top of your animals and hang them up as decorations.

Bottle Top Ladybird Dominoes

Use leftover milk bottle tops to make this cute ladybird
domino game, then play with a friend.

You will need:

16 plastic milk bottle tops
Red paint
A paintbrush
A black washable marker pen

What to do:

1 Paint all 16 bottle tops red and leave to dry.

2 Use the black pen to draw a line down the
middle of each bottle top to make two wings,
and colour in a face.

3 Now add your ladybirds' spots. Copy the
diagram on the back of your sticker sheet –
each domino has a different pattern.

Don't worry if you make a mistake. The game will still work.

How to play:

1 You can play this game with 2–4 players. Shuffle all the dominoes and
give four to each player. Put any that are left over in a pile.

2 The youngest player goes first and picks a domino to put on the table.
The next player has to find a domino with the same number of spots as
one side of the first domino. If they have a domino with a side that
matches, they place it on the table with the matching sides together.
Players can add dominoes to either side.

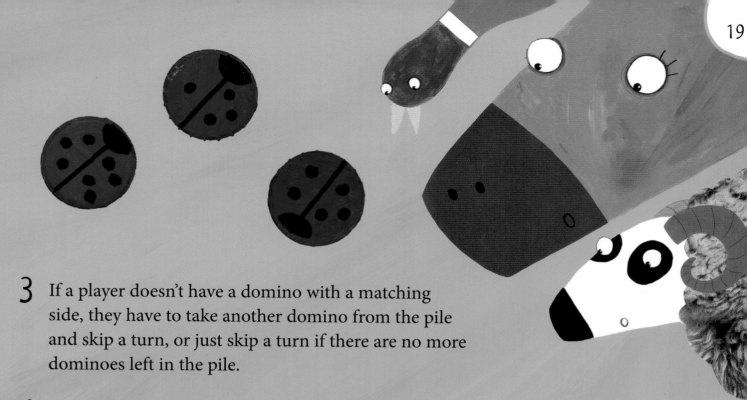

3 If a player doesn't have a domino with a matching side, they have to take another domino from the pile and skip a turn, or just skip a turn if there are no more dominoes left in the pile.

4 The game continues with each player taking turns to add a domino to the table, or picking up a domino from the pile. The winner is the first player to get rid of all their dominoes.

Tips, Tricks and Twists

✳ If you don't have bottle tops, you could use jam jar lids or cut out circles of card instead.

✳ When you've finished your game, store your dominoes in an envelope or box so you don't lose them. Why not decorate it with spots, too – try the techniques on pages 12 and 13.

Paper Cup Phone

But the ladybird had a good idea
And she whispered it into each animal ear.
This 'phone' lets you pass on secret messages. Whisper into
a friend's ear just like the ladybird does!

You will need:

2 paper cups
A sharp pencil
String (about 3–4 metres)
Safety scissors
Two beads or buttons
Paints
Paintbrushes

What to do:

1 Ask a grown-up to carefully poke a hole in the bottom of each cup with the pencil.

2 Tie one of your beads or buttons on to one end of your string. Ask your grown-up to help you thread the string through the hole from the inside of the first cup, so the bead or button sits in the bottom of the cup. You might need to use the pencil to poke the string through.

3 Pull the string so it's all the way through the hole, then ask your grown-up to help you thread it through the hole in the other cup, keeping the second cup the opposite way round to the first cup.

4 Thread your other bead or button on to the end of the string and tie it so it sits in the bottom of your second cup.

5 Now it's time to decorate your phone. How about giving it a farmyard theme? Use the cow sponge print pattern from page 17 or the ladybird spots from pages 12 and 13.

6 To use your phone, hold one cup and give the other to a friend. Stand as far apart as you can, so you are pulling the string tight. Now take turns for one person to speak into their cup, and the other to hold their cup to their ear. The sound of your voice travels along the string!

HELLO! Can you hear me?

Yes, no need to shout!

Tips, Tricks and Twists

★ Make sure the string is pulled tight when you use your phone, otherwise it won't work.

★ Fishing wire works especially well for this, as the sound of your voice can travel easily along it.

✳ If you prefer, you can use empty yoghurt pots instead of paper cups.

Adventure Trail Map

"Open the gate at dead of night,
Pass the horse and then turn right . . ."
Hefty Hugh and Lanky Len have a map of the farmyard. Make your own map!

You will need:

An A4 or A3 sheet of
squared or plain paper
Colouring pens or pencils
Treasure to find (optional)

What to do:

Don't be like Hefty
Hugh and Lanky Len . . .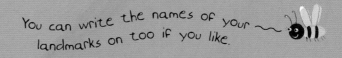

1 Decide what you would like to make
a map of. It could be your garden, a local
park, or even your bedroom. This will be
your location.

2 Look around your location carefully. What
are the main things you can see? Pick three
or four landmarks that you want to mark
on your map.

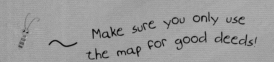 *Make sure you only use
the map for good deeds!*

3 Take your sheet of paper and carefully tear a thin strip off each side to make
rough, torn edges.

4 Time to start drawing. Think carefully about what your location would look like
from above, and where each landmark is. Then draw a simple picture of each
landmark. Add any other details that you think will make the map easier to read,
such as trees or benches in a park, or furniture in a room.

5 Using a different colour pen or pencil, draw a trail
for your friend to follow, with a big red X where you
want them to end up. You can use the stickers from
your sticker sheet if you prefer.

*You can write the names of your
landmarks on too if you like.*

6 Gently crumple up your map then unfold it to make it look old and used.

7 Now give your map to a friend and see if they can follow your trail! You could even hide some treasure or a secret message at the end for them to find.

Hmm . . .
~ which way should I go?

Tips, Tricks and Twists

* If you're nervous about making a mistake, draw your landmarks on to another piece of paper first, then cut them out, position them on top of your map and glue them down.

* Ask a grown-up to save you a used teabag – when it's cool, gently wipe or dab it over your paper to make brown splodges. When the tea dries, your map will look like old paper!

Noisy Kazoo

"NEIGH!" said the horse. "OINK!" said the hog.
"BAA!" said the sheep. "WOOF!" said the dog.
The farmyard is full of different noises! Make a kazoo
using a cardboard tube, then use it to make funny animal sounds.

You will need:

A toilet roll tube
Baking paper
Safety scissors
A rubber band
A sharp pencil
Paints or colouring pens

What to do:

1 Cut a circular piece of baking paper that is large enough to easily fit over one end of the toilet roll tube. Try tracing around the outside of a roll of sticky tape or a wide mug.

2 Place your baking paper circle over one end of your toilet roll tube and wrap the rubber band tightly around it to keep it in place.

3 Ask a grown-up to use the pencil to poke a hole in the side of the tube. This allows the sound to escape.

4 Decorate your kazoo – how about painting it with farmyard colours and adding stickers from your sticker sheet, or covering it with the sponge print cow pattern from page 17?

5 Your kazoo is ready to play. Put the open end up to your mouth and hum – your hum should turn into a funny loud noise. You might need a bit of practice, but once you've got the hang of it, try different sounds to see what noises the kazoo makes. Can you make a mooing cow, a baa-ing sheep, or a quacking duck?

Wow! How does it work?

The sound of your voice makes the baking paper vibrate, which makes the sound louder!

Tips, Tricks and Twists

⭐ Experiment with using different lengths of cardboard tube – try a long kitchen roll tube or cut a toilet roll tube in half. Does the length of the tube affect the sounds you can make?

⭐ Try putting your finger over the hole in the tube while you are humming. What happens to the sound?

⭐ How about painting your kazoo red and adding black spots, then making buzzing noises like a flying ladybird?

Ladybird Wings

Create your very own pair of spotty wings to wear,
then fly around like the ladybird.

— These wings really flap!

You will need:

2 sheets of red A4 card
Safety scissors
A pencil
2 sheets of black A4 card
A hole punch
2 split pins
Ribbon or string (about
    150cm)
Glue

What to do:

1   Draw a large semi-circle on a sheet of red card,
    then cut it out. Place the first piece on top of the
    second sheet of red card and draw around it, then
    cut out the second piece so you have two wings.

2   Cut a sheet of black card in half
    lengthways. With one of the
    long sides closest to you, use
    the hole punch to make two
    holes near the centre, about
    10cm apart, and two more
    holes in each side. ➙

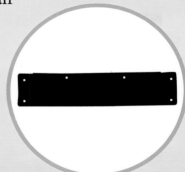

3   Cut two pieces of ribbon, each about 30cm long. Thread the first piece through
    the holes on one side of your black card, and the other piece through the holes
    on the other side. Ask a grown-up to help you position the card so it sits across
    the back of your shoulders then tie the ends of each piece to fit around your arms
    (not too tightly!).

4   Punch a hole in the top corner of each wing, and another hole in each wing about
    3cm further towards the outside. Look at the main picture to see where the holes go.

5   Put a split pin through each wing's outer hole, then through the holes in the middle
    of the black card. Bend the backs so the pieces stay together.

6 Cut a piece of ribbon about 15cm long and thread it through both wings' inner holes from the front. Ask your grown-up to knot the ribbon behind each hole and trim the ends.

7 Cut another piece of ribbon about 40cm long. Tie one end in the middle of the piece that joins the inner holes between the two wings.

8 Cut out four small circles from your remaining sheet of black card and stick two to each wing. You might find it helpful to draw around a glass or a mug.

9 Put on your wings, and reach behind you to grab the long piece of ribbon. Gently pull the ribbon and your wings will flap!

PULL

Tips, Tricks and Twists

✳ To make antennae, wind the bottoms of two pipe cleaners around a plastic hairband, then bend the tops into curls and put the hairband on.

✳ How about dressing in black to look just like the ladybird?

Make Your Own Farm

Once upon a farm . . .
Use an old cereal box to make your very own farm playset!

You will need:

A plastic tray
Yellow and green tissue
  paper
Glue
An empty cereal box
Safety scissors
Colouring pens and pencils
Paint
Paintbrushes
Sticky tape

Make your farmyard:

1 Take a sheet of yellow tissue paper and gently scrunch it up. Open it out and place it on your tray to make the ground of your farmyard. Stick down the corners with glue to hold it in place.

2 Ask a grown-up to help you cut all the way around the top of the cereal box, about 10cm from the top. This top piece will be your barn. Put it to one side to finish in the next section.

If you don't have a cereal box, use plain card instead.

3 Carefully open out the rest of the cereal box and cut along the folds so you have six different pieces. Keep one of the large pieces and one of the long thin pieces, and put the other pieces to one side.

4 Paint your large piece and long thin piece of card blue on one side and leave to dry.

5 Cut your large piece of card into a wobbly oval shape to make a pond, then stick it down in the middle of your farmyard. Add some plants and lilypads, using green paper or scrunched tissue paper.

6 Take your long painted piece of card and cut two thin strips along the long edge, each about 1cm wide.

7 Cut the rest of the painted card into lots of short strips about 1cm wide.

8 Place the long pieces about 1cm apart and glue the short pieces on to them to make a fence like the one in the main picture. Leave about 1cm between each of your short pieces.

Make your barn:

1 Take the top of the cereal box that you set aside earlier. Cut a small rectangle in one of the long sides starting at the edge to make a door.

2 Paint the outside walls of your barn with dark brown paint and leave to dry.

3 Take your second large piece of cereal box and fold it in half. This will be the roof for your barn. Paint it red and leave to dry.

4 Draw lots of little tiles on both sides of your roof. Ask your grown-up to help you stick it to the top of your barn, as shown in the picture.

Make your animals:

1 Draw a horse, a pig, a cow and a sheep on a piece of card and cut them out. You can copy or trace the animals on the back of your sticker page, or draw your own.

2 Draw on details and colour in or paint your animals. You can use the decorating techniques from pages 16 and 17 and the stickers from your sticker sheet.

Add a duck to your pond too – see page 11 for how to make it.

3 Cut a slit in the bottom of your first animal, about 2cm high.

4 Cut a piece of card about 4cm wide and 2cm high, then slot it into the base of your animal to make a cross shape. Then stand your animal up.

5 Cut slits and pieces of card for the rest of your animals, so they can all stand up. Now position them in your farmyard and your playset is ready!

Tips, Tricks and Twists

✳ Make more animals to go on your farm by following steps 1 to 5 above. How about making a goose, some cats, or a whole herd of sheep?

★ You could also make Hefty Hugh and Lanky Len, or use dolls or action figures.

✳ Why not act out the story from *What the Ladybird Heard* – or make up your own farmyard story!

First published 2020 by Macmillan Children's Books
an imprint of Pan Macmillan
The Smithson, 6 Briset Street, London EC1M 5NR
Associated companies throughout the world
www.panmacmillan.com

ISBN: 978-1-5290-2396-1

A CIP catalogue record for this book is available from the British Library.

Printed in China.

Paper Plate Duck Pond

Adventure Trail Map

Here are some extra stickers to decorate your crafts.

You might find these templates helpful when making some of your crafts.
Have a look on page 3 to find out how to use them.

Lots of Ladybirds

Paper Plate Duck Pond

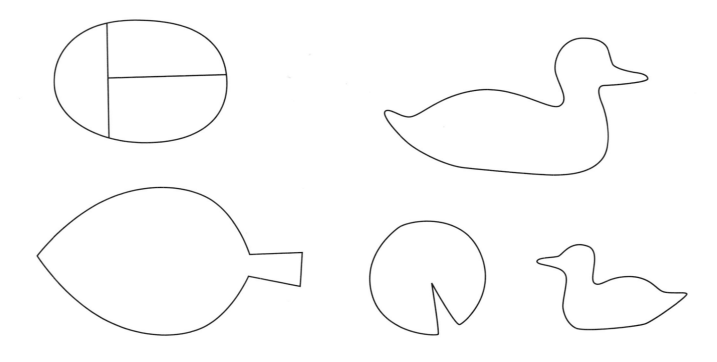

Clucking Hen

You can copy these outlines to make animals pictures to use in
Arty Animals and Make Your Own Farm.

You can copy these ladybird spots to make your Bottle Top Ladybird dominoes.

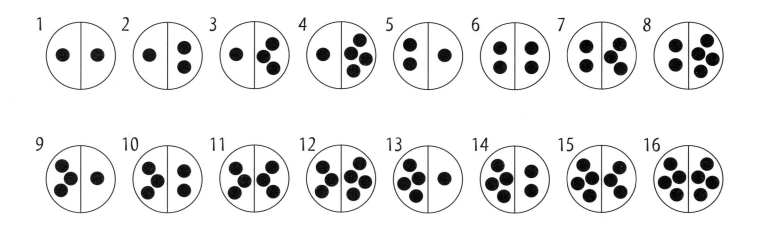

Make Your Own Farm

You can use these stickers to decorate the Noisy Kazoo, Make Your Own Farm and more!

These eyes will come in handy for lots of your crafts, like Lots of Ladybirds, Arty Animals and more!